RISING★STARS

ASSESSMENT

Reading

Progress Tests

Year

5

Helen Lewis

Series Advisors: Cornwall Learning

Rising Stars UK Ltd, part of Hodder Education,
an Hachette UK Company
Carmelite House, 50 Victoria Embankment, London EC4Y 0DZ

www.risingstars-uk.com

Published 2014
Reprinted 2014 (four times), 2015 (seven times)

Author: Helen Lewis
Educational consultants: Shareen Mayers, Sutton Improvement and Support Services, and Sara Moult, Cornwall Learning
Accessibility reviewer: Vivien Kilburn
Editorial: Lesley Densham for Green Desert Ltd and Sarah Davies
Design: Andy Wilson for Green Desert Ltd
Illustrations: David Woodroffe
Photos: istockphoto.com (page 40) and NASA/Johns Hopkins University Applied Physics Laboratory/Carnegie Institution of Washington (page 16)
Cover design: Burville-Riley Partnership

Acknowledgements:
p9 *Growing Up in Ancient Greece*, adapted from the original text on the BBC History website (www.bbc.co.uk); p10 extract from *Oliver Twist* by Charles Dickens, retold by Mary Sebag-Montefiore, Copyright © 2006 Usborne Publishing. Reproduced by permission of the author Usborne Publishing, 83-85 Saffron Hill, London EC1N 8RT; p15 extract from *Colly's Barn* by Michael Morpurgo; p16 Mercury, adapted from *Space Frontiers: Our Solar System* by Helen Whittaker; p21 *The Missing Boy* by Sharon Olds; p22 extract from the first chapter of Room 13 by Robert Swindells; p27 *The Legend of the Fens*, adapted from *The Legend of the Fens* on E2BN's *Myths and Legends* website (www.myths.e2bn.org/mythsandlegends); p28 *Why Do You Stay Up So Late?* by Don Paterson, Copyright © Don Paterson 2009. Reproduced by permission of the author c/o Rogers, Coleridge & White Ltd., 20 Powis Mews, London W11 1JN; p33 *The Cats' Protection League* by Roger McGough, from Bad, Bad Cats (© Roger McGough 1997) is printed by permission of United Agents (www.unitedagents.co.uk) on behalf of Roger McGough; p34 extract from chapter four of *Tom's Midnight Garden* by Philippa Pearce, (OUP, 2008), copyright © Oxford University Press 1958, reproduced by permission of Oxford University Press; p39 *The Blind Man and the Hunter*, a traditional story from West Africa, adapted from *Tales of Wisdom and Wonder*, retold by Hugh Lupton; p40 *Five Freaky Forces of Nature*, adapted from *Ten Freaky Forces of Nature* by Douglas E. Richards from ww.kids.nationalgeographic.com, Douglas Richards/National Geographic Creative

Every effort has been made to trace copyright holders and obtain their permission for the use of copyright materials. The author and publisher will gladly receive information enabling them to rectify any error or omission in subsequent editions.

Rising Stars is grateful to the following people and schools who contributed to the development of these materials:
Plumcroft Primary School, London; St Helens Teaching Schools Alliance; St Nicholas CE Primary School, Chislehurst; St Margaret's CE Primary School, Heywood, Rochdale; Tennyson Road Primary School, Luton

British Library Cataloguing in Publication Data.
A CIP record for this book is available from the British Library.
ISBN: 978 1 78339 100 4

Printed by Ashford Colour Press

Contents

Introduction

Why use Rising Stars Assessment Progress Tests?

The *Rising Stars Assessment Reading Progress Tests* have been developed to support teachers assess the progress their pupils are making against the reading and comprehension requirements of the 2014 National Curriculum Programme of Study for English in Years 2 to 6. Separate progress tests are available to cover the requirements for grammar, punctuation, spelling and vocabulary. For Year 1 there is a single set of progress tests for English. These include reading, spelling, and grammar, punctuation and vocabulary tests. All *Rising Stars Assessment Progress Tests* are designed to support effective classroom assessment and are easy to use and mark.

The *Rising Stars Assessment Reading Progress Tests* include one test for each half term. All the tests have been:

- written by primary English assessment specialists
- reviewed by primary English curriculum and assessment experts.

How do the tests track progress?

The results data from the tests can be used to track progress. They show whether pupils are making the expected progress for their year, more than expected progress or less than expected progress. This data can then be used alongside other evidence to enable effective planning of future teaching and learning, for reporting to parents and as evidence for Ofsted inspections. If teachers are using the CD-ROM version of the tests, the results data can be keyed into the Progress Tracker (see pages 6–7 for more information) which automatically shows the progress of individual pupils against the Programme of Study and the results for all pupils by question and test. Data can also be exported into the school's management information system (MIS).

About the Reading Progress Tests

The tests are written to cover the requirements of the Programme of Study for the 2014 National Curriculum including the Appendices for English. There is a separate test for each half term. The number of marks for each test is as follows:

Year 2	Year 3	Year 4	Year 5	Year 6
15	20	20	20	20

The style of the tests mirrors that of the tests pupils will take at the end of Key Stages 1 and 2. Each test has two extracts with questions. The extracts used in the tests are authentic, age-appropriate ones and include fiction, poetry and non-fiction including those by well-known children's authors. Where possible the texts have been chosen to link to other subjects in the National Curriculum, in particular geography, history and science. The tests assess across a range of skills as exemplified by the assessment focuses for reading. The assessment focuses covered are:

AF2: understand, describe, select or retrieve information, events or ideas from texts and use quotation and reference to text;

AF3: deduce, infer or interpret information, events or ideas from texts;

AF4: identify and comment on the structure and organisation of texts, including grammatical and presentational features at text level;

AF5: explain and comment on writers' uses of language, including grammatical and literary features at word and sentence level;

AF6: identify and comment on writers' purposes and viewpoints and the overall effect of the text on the reader;

AF7: relate texts to their social, cultural and historical contexts and literary traditions.

From 2016 the national tests will use strands instead of assessment focuses. Full details of which AF and strand each question assesses can be found in the Coverage grid on page 57.

Test demand

Test demand increases both within tests and across the year, which means that tests at the beginning of the year are easier than those at the end of the year. Within each test the Part A extract and questions is easier than the Part B extract and questions. As the year progresses the extracts and questions become increasingly more difficult.

Tracking progress

The marks pupils score in the tests can be used to track how they are progressing against the expected outcomes for their year group. The marks for each test have been split into three progress zones:

- less than expected progress
- expected progress
- more than expected progress.

The zones for each year group are as follows:

	Zone mark range		
	Less than expected progress	Expected progress	More than expected progress
Year 2	0–7	8–12	13–15
Year 3	0–10	11–16	17–20
Year 4	0–10	11–16	17–20
Year 5	0–10	11–16	17–20
Year 6	0–10	11–16	17–20

The table gives the mark ranges for the progress zones for each test which you can use to see how well each pupil is doing in each test. If pupils are making the expected progress for their year they will be consistently scoring marks in the middle zone of marks in the tests. The higher the mark in the zone, the more secure you can be that they are making expected progress.

How to use the Reading Progress Tests

Preparation and timings

1 Make enough copies of the test(s) for each pupil to have their own copy.
2 Hand out the papers and ensure pupils are seated appropriately so that they can't see each other's papers.

3 Pupils will need pens or pencils and erasers. Encourage pupils to cross out answers rather than rub them out.

4 There are no time limits for the tests but normal practice is to allow a minute per mark for written tests. Help with reading may be given using the same rules as when providing a reader with the DfE KS2 tests.

Supporting pupils during the tests

Before the test explain to the pupils that the test is an opportunity to show what they know, understand and can do. They should try to answer all the questions but should not worry if there are some they can't do.

Many pupils will be able to work independently in the tests, with minimal support from the teacher or a teaching assistant. However, pupils should be encouraged to 'have a go' at a question, or to move on to a fresh question if they appear to be stuck, to ensure that no pupil becomes distressed.

It is important that pupils receive appropriate support, but are not unfairly advantaged or disadvantaged. Throughout the tests, therefore, the teacher may read, explain or sign to a pupil any parts of the test that include instructions, for example by demonstrating how to circle an answer.

With younger age groups you may also consider using the version of the test on the CD-ROM and projecting it onto a whiteboard to support a whole class or group to take the tests. You may choose to refer to the words on the whiteboard and read them aloud so that pupils can follow them on the screen and on their own test paper and then write their answers on their papers individually.

Marking the tests

Use the detailed mark scheme and your professional judgement to award marks. Do not award half marks.

It is useful to use peer marking of test questions from time to time. Pupils should exchange test sheets and mark them as you read out the question and answer. You will need to check that pupils are marking accurately. This approach also provides an opportunity to recap on any questions that pupils found difficult to answer.

Feeding back to pupils

Once the test has been marked, use a five-minute feedback session with the pupils to help them review their answers. Wherever possible pupils should be encouraged to make their own corrections as in this way they will become more aware of their own strengths and weaknesses. Agree with each pupil what they did well in the test and what the targets are for them to improve. A template Pupil progress sheet is provided on page 8 for this purpose.

Using the Progress Tracker

The table on page 5 gives the mark ranges for the progress zones for each test which you can use to see how well each pupil is doing in each test. If pupils are making the expected progress for their year they will be consistently scoring marks in the middle zone of marks in the tests.

The higher the mark in the zone, the more secure you can be that they are making expected progress.

The CD-ROM version of *Reading Progress Tests* includes an interactive Progress Tracker, which allows you to enter the marks for each question for each test by pupil. This then automatically shows you which zone the pupil is in and also the zone distribution for the class so that you can track the progress of individual pupils and the whole class.

The Progress Tracker also enables you to review the marks for each question so that you can identify areas where some or all pupils may need further support and areas where some or all pupils are ready to be stretched further. Questions in the reading tests are mapped to the *Rising Stars Progression Framework for Reading*. These statements originate from the Programme of Study and enable you to see which specific aspect of reading is being assessed. The statements can be accessed by rolling over the Progression Framework codes below the question number.

If required, data from the tests can be exported into the school's management information system (MIS) so that it can be used alongside other data in whole school monitoring including the monitoring of specific groups of pupils, such as Pupil Premium.

Full details about the Progress Tracker are provided on the CD-ROM.

Pupil progress sheet

Name: _____ Class: _____ Date: _____

Test name: _____ Test number: _____ My mark: _____

What I did well in the test:

_____

_____

_____

What I need to do to improve:

1. _____

2. _____

3. _____

- -

Pupil progress sheet

Name: _____ Class: _____ Date: _____

Test name: _____ Test number: _____ My mark: _____

What I did well in the test:

_____

_____

_____

What I need to do to improve:

1. _____

2. _____

3. _____

This text is adapted from the original text on the BBC Primary History website (www.bbc.co.uk/schools/primaryhistory).

Growing Up in Ancient Greece

Sons and daughters

Many Greek parents wanted boy children. A son would look after his parents in old age. A daughter went away when she married and had to take a wedding gift or dowry. This could be expensive, if a family had lots of daughters.

A father could decide whether or not the family kept a new baby. Unwanted or weak babies were sometimes left to die outdoors. Anyone finding an abandoned baby could adopt it and take it home, perhaps to raise it as a slave. If a couple were rich, they might hire a poor neighbour or a slave to nurse a new baby.

> **Glossary**
>
> **archaeologist** – someone who finds out about the lives of people from the distant past by finding and studying things they left behind

Going to school

At the age of three, children were given small jugs - a sign that babyhood was over. Boys started school at the age of seven. Girls were taught at home by their mothers. A few girls learned to read and write, but many did not. Schoolteachers needed payment, so poor boys did not get much education. A wealthy family would send a slave to walk to school with the boys. The slave would stay at school to keep an eye on them during lessons. Most Greek schools had fewer than twenty boys and classes were often held outdoors.

What did Greek children learn?

Girls learned housework, cooking and skills such as weaving at home. Boys at school learned reading, writing, arithmetic, music and poetry. Part of their lessons included learning stories and poems by heart. They wrote on wooden tablets covered with soft wax, using a pointed stick called a stylus. They used an abacus, with beads strung on wires or wooden rods, to help with maths.

Boys did athletics, to keep fit and prepare them for war as soldiers. They ran, jumped, wrestled and practised throwing a spear and a discus. They trained on a sports ground called a gymnasium.

Children's toys

We know about some Greek toys from pictures on pottery vases and from objects found by **archaeologists**. Children played with small pottery figures and dolls made of rags, wood, wax or clay - some dolls had moveable arms and legs. Other toys were rattles, hoops, yo-yos, and hobby horses (a 'pretend horse' made from a stick).

Children played with balls made from tied-up rags or a blown-up pig's bladder. The anklebones of sheep or goats made 'knucklebones' or five-stones. There are pictures of children with pets, such as dogs, geese and chickens.

This text is from *Oliver Twist* by Charles Dickens, retold by Mary Sebag-Montefiore.

Oliver Twist

Oliver Twist was an orphan. He lived a miserable life in a workhouse before being placed with an undertaker where he was badly treated. He ran away and travelled to London…

At last he reached the city. His sore feet were bleeding and his clothes were worn to shreds. He watched people jostling around market stalls and shops, so busy that no one noticed him.

He collapsed on a cold doorstep, too exhausted to beg. Delicious smells floated by from a bakery. Oliver staggered up to the window, where shelves groaned with piles of freshly-made bread, cakes, buns and pies. He stared at them longingly.

A boy about the same age, with sharp eyes and a swaggering walk, strolled over. 'Hungry?' he asked.

'Very,' gasped Oliver.

To Oliver's astonishment, the boy pulled a wad of money out of his pocket.

'I'll get you something. Wait here.'

The boy returned with a bag crammed with hot meat pies.

'I'm Dodger,' said the boy, as Oliver gobbled the food. 'You?'

'Oliver Twist.'

'Got a bed tonight, Oliver?'

'No.'

'Got any family?'

'No one at all.'

'I know a kind gentleman who'll take you in. He won't want any rent, either.'

'That's generous!' exclaimed Oliver. He followed Dodger down a maze of narrow alleys, where foul smells filled the air and swarms of ragged urchins played in slimy, oozing gutters. Men and women staggered around, cursing loudly.

It looked so dirty, Oliver almost wished he hadn't come, but he had nowhere else to go. Finally, they reached a crumbling house. Dodger led him up a rickety staircase to a dark room.

Through a cloud of sizzling fumes, Oliver spied a gnarled old man. He was wearing a grubby blue coat and frying sausages over a fire.

Behind him, a group of boys danced and dodged, playing a game. The old man's coat had lots of pockets, stuffed with hankies, wallets and pens and the boys were trying to pull them out without him noticing.

'Hey, Fagin,' yelled Dodger. 'This is Oliver.'

'Hello, Oliver.' Fagin bared his teeth in a leering grin. 'Want to play?'

'Yes sir,' said Oliver politely. He waited until Fagin bent over the frying pan, crept up … and delicately drew out a hanky.

'You're a natural!' chuckled Fagin. 'Come near the fire. Have a sausage!'

Name:	Class:	Date:

Growing Up in Ancient Greece

1 Give **one** reason why many Greek parents wanted sons rather than daughters.

_____

2b
1 mark

2 In Ancient Greece which member of the family could decide whether to keep a new baby?

_____

2b
1 mark

3 Who was most likely to go to school in Ancient Greece? Tick the **best** answer.

boys and girls aged seven and over ☐

boys and girls whose parents were rich ☐

boys whose parents were not poor ☐

girls whose parents were not poor ☐

2d
1 mark

4 Why do you think classes in Ancient Greek schools were often held outdoors? Tick the **best** answer.

So that anyone could join in. ☐

Because schools didn't have enough money to build classrooms. ☐

Because the weather was warm and dry. ☐

Because classes were so large they needed lots of space. ☐

2d
1 mark

5 How do we know about children's toys in ancient Greece? Give **two** sources of evidence.

_____

2b
1 mark

/ 5
Total for this page

6 The writer has used subheadings. These are *Sons and daughters, Going to school, What did Greek children learn?* and *Children's toys.*

Why do you think the writer chose to use subheadings?

_____

2f

1 mark

7 Look at the section headed: *What did Greek children learn?*
What points is the writer trying to make about what children learned in Ancient Greece? Tick **three**.

Boys started school at the age of seven. ☐

Many school subjects from Ancient Greece are still studied in schools today. ☐

Girls learned different things to boys. ☐

Ancient Greek children needed help with maths. ☐

Some of the equipment used in Ancient Greek schools is no longer used in schools today. ☐

2b

1 mark

8 Where would you expect to find this text? Tick the **best** answer.

in a travel brochure ☐

in a newspaper ☐

in a magazine ☐

in a history book ☐

2f

1 mark

9 Girls in Ancient Greece had a better life than boys.

Explain whether you think this is **true** or **not true**, using the text to support your answer.

_____

_____

_____

2d

2 marks

/ 10

Total for this test

12

Name:	Class:	Date:

Oliver Twist

1 At the beginning of the passage Oliver is tired and hungry.

a) How can you tell he is tired? Give **one** way.

_____

2a

1 mark

b) How can you tell he is hungry? Give **one** way.

_____

2a

1 mark

2 Oliver and Dodger are about the same age. What is **different** about them? Describe **two** things.

_____

_____

2d

1 mark

3 Look at the paragraph beginning: *'That's generous!' exclaimed Oliver.*

Find and **copy a phrase** that means the same as 'children wearing tattered clothes'.

_____

2a

1 mark

/ 4

Total for this page

13

4 *Fagin bared his teeth in a leering grin.*

What impression does this sentence give of Fagin? Tick **one**.

He is friendly. ☐

He is happy. ☐

He is angry. ☐

He is sly. ☐

☐ 2g
1 mark

---

5 Look at the last three lines of the text, from '*Yes sir,*' to the end.
What do you find out about Oliver? Write **two** things.

1 _____

2 _____

☐ 2b
1 mark

---

6 How might Oliver feel at the end of the passage? Why?

_____

_____

☐ 2d
1 mark

---

7 What genre does this text belong to? Explain how you know, using the text to help you answer.

_____

_____

☐ 2f
2 marks

---

8 The story is set in London in the 19th century. Think about the whole passage. What impression of 19th century London is the writer trying to create?

_____

_____

☐ 2c
1 mark

☐ / 10
Total for this test

14

This text is from *Colly's Barn* by Michael Morpurgo.

Colly's Barn

All night, as the storm raged outside, the birds in the barn huddled together in their nests, burying their heads in each other to blot out the sound of the thunder. The wind whined and whistled through the eaves, the walls shuddered and the beams creaked and groaned. But Screecher and Colly were not worried. They'd been through storms like this before and the old barn had held together.

Screecher thought the worst of it was over. He was peering through a crack in the wall, looking for the first light of dawn on the distant hills, when lightning struck. In one blinding flash night was turned to day. A deafening clap of thunder shook the barn and a fireball glowing orange and blue rolled around the barn and disappeared through the door.

Through the smoke Screecher could see that the crack in the wall was suddenly a gaping hole and above him the roof was open to the rain.

Grandad's bad knee kept him in bed the next morning and Annie was at school when her father and mother discovered the hole in the barn wall.

'Lucky it didn't catch fire,' said Annie's mother.

'Might have been better if it had,' said her father. 'One way or another that barn's got to come down now. I've been saying it for years.'

'You could patch it up,' Annie's mother replied.

Her father shook his head. 'Waste of time and money. New modern shed, that's what we need. I'll have a bulldozer in, we'll soon have it down.'

'Grandad won't like it,' she said. 'You know how much he likes old buildings. I don't want you upsetting him again.'

'It's just a tumbledown old barn,' he said. 'Anyway, Grandad won't know till it's all over. He won't be out of bed for a couple of days, not with his knee like it is. And not a word to Annie, she tells him everything. Thick as thieves they are, those two.'

This text is adapted from *Space Frontiers: Our Solar System* by Helen Whittaker.

Mercury

Tiny Mercury, the planet nearest to the Sun, is also the fastest moving. It is named after the speedy, wing-heeled messenger of the Roman gods.

The extreme planet

Mercury is the planet with the widest temperature range. During the day, temperatures can reach a sweltering 427°C, which is far hotter than an oven. As Mercury has no atmosphere to trap the heat, the heat escapes back out into space at night. Temperatures plummet to –173°C, which is much colder than the coldest temperature ever recorded on Earth.

Destination Mercury

From Mercury, the Sun looks three times larger than it does when seen from Earth. However, you would need a very special spacesuit to take in this view on Mercury. It would not only need to protect you from the vacuum of space and the planet's extreme temperatures, but also from the Sun's deadly **radiation**, which is stronger on Mercury than on any other planet in the solar system.

Massive impact

The largest feature on Mercury is the Caloris Basin, an impact crater 1,500 km across. It was created billions of years ago when a large **asteroid** crashed into Mercury. On the opposite side of the planet are rocky ridges caused by shock waves from the impact.

Viewing Mercury from Earth

As Mercury is very close to the Sun, it is not easy viewing it from Earth, except at twilight. Mercury also appears indirectly 13 times every century when it passes across the face of the Sun. This event is called a transit.

FACTS AND FIGURES

Name: Mercury

History: known since prehistoric times, named after the messenger of the Roman gods

Type of body: terrestrial planet

Diameter: 4,879.4 km

Atmosphere: almost none

Number of moons: 0

Average distance from the Sun: 57.9 million km

Length of day: 58.646 Earth days

Length of year: 87.97 Earth days

Temperature range: –173°C to 427°C

DID YOU KNOW?

Mercury orbits the Sun at an average speed of 172,332 km per hour. This is nearly 188 times faster than a jumbo jet.

GLOSSARY

asteroid – a lump of rock orbiting the Sun
radiation – energy given out in the form of particles or waves
terrestrial – Earth-like

Name:	Class:	Date:

Colly's Barn

1 What damaged the barn during the storm? Tick **one**.

wind ☐ rain ☐ thunder ☐ lightning ☐

2b
1 mark

2 Who do you think Colly and Screecher are? Explain why you think this, using the text to help you.

_____

_____

2d
2 marks

3 *The wind whined and whistled through the eaves.*

What language effects does the writer use in this sentence? Give **two**.

1 _____

2 _____

2g
1 mark

4 Look at the second paragraph, beginning: *Screecher thought...*

How does the writer make this paragraph exciting? Write **one** way, explaining how it adds to the excitement.

_____

2g
1 mark

5 Why doesn't Annie's mother want the barn to be pulled down?
Tick the **best** answer.

She likes the old barn. ☐

She loves Grandad. ☐

She wants to save money. ☐

She doesn't like modern sheds. ☐

2d
1 mark

/ 6
Total for this page

6   *'It's just a tumbledown old barn,' he said.*

Think about the word *tumbledown*. Which of the following could **not** replace it in the passage? Tick **one**.

ramshackle ☐   dilapidated ☐

pristine ☐   weather-beaten ☐

2a
1 mark

---

7   *And not a word to Annie, she tells him everything. Thick as thieves they are, those two.*

What does *thick as thieves* tell you about Annie and her grandfather? Tick **one**.

They are dishonest. ☐   They are very close. ☐

They are not very clever. ☐   They don't get on well. ☐

2a
1 mark

---

8   **Number** these events to show **the order** in which they happen. The first one has been done for you.

1	The birds huddle together in their nests.
☐	Annie's father decides to pull down the barn.
☐	Screecher peers through a crack in the wall.
☐	Annie's father and mother discover the hole in the barn wall.
☐	The barn gets damaged.

2f
1 mark

---

9   Which of the following descriptions best fits this passage? Tick **one**.

a comedy ☐   a parable ☐

a fable ☐   an animal story ☐

2f
1 mark

/ 10
Total for this test

Name:	Class:	Date:

Mercury

1 How did Mercury get its name?

_____

_____

2b
1 mark

2 Read the statements about Mercury in the table below.

Put a tick next to each statement that is supported by the text.
Put a cross next to each statement that is **not** supported by the text.

Statement	✓ or ✗
Mercury is the largest planet.	
Mercury is the fastest moving planet.	
Mercury is the planet closest to the Sun.	
Mercury is the hottest planet.	
Mercury is the planet with the widest range of temperatures.	

2b
2 marks

3 Draw lines to match the measurement to the fact. One has been done for you.

Measurement	Fact
427°C	the night-time temperature on Mercury
1,500 km	the daytime temperature on Mercury
4,879.4 km	the average speed at which Mercury orbits the Sun
172,332 km per hour	the diameter of Mercury
−173°C	the width of the Caloris Basin

2b
1 mark

/ 4
Total for this page

4 Why do you think the Sun looks three times larger from Mercury than it does from Earth?

_____

_____

2d
1 mark

5 The writer has used subheadings (for example, *Destination Mercury*) and feature boxes (for example, *Facts and figures*).

Why do you think the writer chose to organise the text in this way?

_____

2f
1 mark

6 What type of text is this? Tick **one**.

an argument ☐   a set of instructions ☐

a report ☐   a recount ☐

an explanation ☐

2f
1 mark

7 Read the paragraph headed *Viewing Mercury from Earth*.

What **main** point is the writer trying to make? Tick **one**.

Mercury is very close to the Sun. ☐

You can't see Mercury from Earth very often. ☐

Sometimes Mercury passes across the face of the Sun. ☐

Mercury appears indirectly 13 times every century. ☐

2b
1 mark

8 **It would be a challenge for humans to visit Mercury.**

How do you know this? Explain as fully as you can, using the text to help you.

_____

_____

2d
2 marks

/ 10
Total for this test

This poem is by Sharon Olds.

The Missing Boy

(for Etan Patz)

Every time we take the bus
my son sees the picture of the missing boy.
He looks at it like a mirror – the dark
straw hair, the pale skin,
the blue eyes, the electric-blue sneakers with
slashes of jagged gold. But of course that
kid is little, only six and a half,
an age when things can happen to you,
when you're not really safe, and our son is seven,
practically fully grown – why, he would
tower over that kid if they could
find him and bring him right here on this bus and
stand them together. He holds to the pole,
wishing for that, the tape on the poster
gleaming over his head, beginning to
melt at the centre and curl at the edges as it
ages. At night, when I put him to bed,
my son holds my hand tight
and says he's sure that kid's all right,
nothing to worry about, he just
hopes he's getting the food he likes,
not just any old food, but the food
he likes the most, the food he is used to.

This text is from the first chapter of *Room 13* by Robert Swindells.

Room 13

This is what Fliss dreamed the night before the second year went to Whitby.

She was walking on a road high above the sea. It was dark. She was alone. Waves were breaking at the foot of cliffs to her left, and further out, the moonlight made a silver path on the water.

In front of her was a house. It was a tall house, looming blackly against the sky. There were many windows, all of them dark.

Fliss was afraid. She didn't want to go inside the house. She didn't even want to walk past but she had no control over her feet. They seemed to go by themselves, forcing her on.

She came to a gate. It was made of iron, worked into curly patterns. Near the top was a bit that was supposed to be a bird in flight - a seagull perhaps - but the gate had been painted black, and the paint had run and hardened into little stalactites along the bird's wings, making it look like a bat.

The gate opened by itself, and as she went through Fliss heard a voice that whispered, 'The Gate of Fate.' She was drawn along a short pathway and up some stone steps to the front door, which also opened by itself. 'The Keep of Sleep,' whispered the voice.

The door closed silently behind her. Moonlight shone coldly through a stained-glass panel into a gloomy hallway. At the far end were stairs that went up into blackness. She didn't want to climb that stairway but her feet drew her along the hallway and up.

She came to a landing with doors. The stairs took a turn and went on up. As Fliss climbed, it grew colder. There was another landing, more doors and another turn in the stair. Upward to a third landing, then a fourth, and then there were no more stairs. She was at the top of the house. There were four doors, each with a number. 10, 11, 12, 13. As she read the numbers, door 13 swung inward with a squeal. 'No!' she whispered, but it was no use. Her feet carried her over the threshold and the voice hissed, 'The Room of Doom.'

In the room was a table. On the table stood a long, pale box. Fliss thought she knew what it was. It filled her with horror, and she whimpered helplessly as her feet drew her towards it. When she was close she saw a shape in the box and there was a smell like damp earth. When she was very close the voice whispered, 'The Bed of Dread,' and then the shape sat up and reached out for her and she screamed. Her screams woke her and she lay damp and trembling in her bed.

Name:	Class:	Date:

The Missing Boy

1   Where did the boy and his mother see the poster?

_____

2b   1 mark

2   The poet says that her son looks at the picture of the missing boy *like a mirror.* What does she mean? Tick **one**.

The poster is shiny. ☐

Her son looks at the poster for a long time. ☐

The boy in the poster looks like her son. ☐

Her son can see his reflection in the poster. ☐

2g   1 mark

3   Describe **two** ways in which the poet's son and the missing boy look alike.

1 _____

2 _____

2b   1 mark

4   a) Do you think the poet believes her seven-year-old son is *practically fully grown*?

_____

2d   1 mark

b) Why do you think the poet describes her son in this way?

_____

2g   1 mark

/ 5   Total for this page

5 Tick to show whether the following sentences are **true** or **false**.
The first one has been done for you.

	True	False
The poet's son is a lot older than the missing boy.		✓
The poet's son finds the poster upsetting.		
The poster has been on the bus for a long time.		
The poet's son knows the missing boy.		

2d
2 marks

6 Read these lines from the end of the poem.

At night, when I put him to bed,
my son holds my hand tight
and says he's sure that kid's all right,
nothing to worry about, he just
hopes he's getting the food he likes,
not just any old food, but the food
he likes the most, the food he is used to.

Underline the phrase that shows that the poet's son **is**, in fact, worried.

2g
1 mark

7 Think about the whole poem. Who or what is the poem **mainly** about?
Tick the **best** answer.

a bus ☐

a boy who has gone missing ☐

a poster ☐

the poet's son ☐

2c
1 mark

8 How would you describe this poem? Tick the **best** answer.

humorous ☐   magical ☐

realistic ☐   rhyming ☐

2f
1 mark

/ 10
Total for this test

Name:	Class:	Date:

Room 13

1 Which of these words does the writer use to describe Fliss? Tick **two**.

tall ☐   pale ☐   dark ☐

alone ☐   afraid ☐

2b
1 mark

2 This passage opens the first chapter of the story. What purpose do you think this passage serves in the story as a whole? Tick the **best** answer.

to introduce the main characters in the story ☐

to describe the setting of the story ☐

to set the mood of the story ☐

to tell the reader what Fliss is like ☐

to explain what happened before the story began ☐

2f
1 mark

3 Look at the paragraph beginning: *She came to a landing with doors ...*

How does the writer make this paragraph scary? Write **one** way, explaining how it adds to the scariness.

_____

_____

2g
2 marks

4 Tick to show whether the following sentences about Fliss's dream are **true** or **false**. The first one has been done for you.

	True	False
The house is near the sea.	✓	
The animal depicted on the gate is a bat.		
Fliss pushes open the door to Room 13.		
Fliss is afraid of Room 13 even before she sees what is inside.		

2b
1 mark

/ 5
Total for this page

5 Look at the penultimate paragraph (the one before the last) beginning:
She came to… **Find** and **copy a phrase** that shows that Fliss has no control over what she does.

_____

2a
1 mark

6 Look at the last paragraph beginning: *In the room…*

Find and **copy a phrase** that means the same as *covered in sweat and shaking*.

_____

2a
1 mark

7 Why does the writer include the whispering voice?

_____

2g
1 mark

8 Look again at the last paragraph beginning: *In the room…* What do you think the *long, pale box* is? Explain why you think this, using the text to help you.

_____

_____

2d
2 marks

/ 10
Total for this test

This text is adapted from *The Legend of the Fens* on E2BN's *Myths and Legends* website (www.myths.e2bn.org/mythsandlegends).

The Legend of the Fens

The Fens, a large area of flat, low-lying land in eastern England, stretch from Lincoln in the north to Cambridge in the south. Nowadays only a complicated drainage system prevents the Fens from becoming water logged. However, legend has it that the Fens were once much drier.

Almost two thousand years ago, Britain was ruled by the Romans, but the Fens were still ruled by the Celtic chief, Mandru. The Romans wanted to take advantage of the Fens' resources: large areas of woodland, a fertile soil and lakes brimming with fish. The Fens were worth the time and effort it would take to claim them, or so the Romans thought.

The Roman Emperor Valerian ordered that Mandru's daughter, Rowena, be captured and forced into slavery. On hearing of his daughter's capture, Mandru gathered his warriors together. They made plans to overthrow the Romans, but before they could carry them out, the Romans captured them.

The captured Celts were put to death - all except Mandru, who managed to escape. He went into hiding and carefully laid his plans. Unlike the Romans, he knew how to engage with the local gods of water and the sky.

Several months later, a stranger came to town warning all the Celts to leave before nightfall. That night, those who had stayed were awoken by a great gale; they saw the town gates had been opened, so they took a chance and made their escape.

They met up with more Celts who had escaped from other settlements. Some were unsure of what to do next, but the stranger appeared again and revealed himself as Mandru. He told them the gods were very angry and that they must make haste to higher ground immediately.

The power of the storm increased and, at midday, the Romans thought they saw a cloud moving swiftly towards them. The cloud turned into a great wall of swirling water, which swept up everything in its path, including the Romans and their houses. Where there had been forest, the land appeared like a sea scattered with small islands.

Mandru led his countrymen back, in triumph, to these lands. The damp atmosphere often saw the Fens covered with a thick, long-lasting mist. The hardy and resourceful Celts stayed in these lands, using all their skill as fishermen and hunters to survive the hostile conditions.

Although the Romans drained parts of the Fens, large areas were left alone. After all, you never quite knew what was lurking in the misty vapour of the Fenland night!

This poem is by Don Paterson.

Why Do You Stay Up So Late?

(For Russ)

I'll tell you, if you really want to know:
remember that day you lost two years ago
at the rockpool where you sat and played the jeweller
with all those stones you'd stolen from the shore?
Most of them went dark and nothing more,
but sometimes one would blink the secret colour
it had locked up somewhere in its stony sleep.
This is how you knew the ones to keep.

So I collect the dull things of the day
in which I see some possibility
but which are dead and which have the surprise
I don't know, and I've no pool to help me tell—
so I look at them and look at them until
one thing makes a mirror in my eyes
then I paint it with the tear to make it bright.
This is why I sit up through the night.

Name:	Class:	Date:

The Legend of the Fens

1 What are the Fens?

_____

2b
1 mark

2 Look at the second paragraph, beginning: *Almost two thousand years ago…*

Find and **copy a phrase** that hints that not everything will go to plan for the Romans.

_____

2g
1 mark

3 Look at the fourth paragraph, beginning: *The captured Celts…*

What do you find out about Mandru? Write **two** things.

1 _____

2 _____

2b
1 mark

4 Why did Mandru go into hiding?

_____

2d
1 mark

5 *The hardy and resourceful Celts stayed in these lands, using all their skill as fishermen and hunters to survive the hostile conditions.*

What does the phrase *the hardy and resourceful Celts* show about the writer's attitude towards the Celts? Tick **one**.

The writer doesn't understand why the Celts went back to the Fens. ☐

The writer thinks the Celts were uncivilised. ☐

The writer thinks the Celts were strange. ☐

The writer admires the Celts. ☐

2g
1 mark

/ 5
Total for this page

6   **Number** these events to show **the order** in which they happen in the story. The first one has been done for you.

☐ A stranger came to town with a warning.

1 The Romans captured Mandru's daughter, Rowena.

☐ The Romans captured Mandru and his warriors.

☐ Mandru made plans to overthrow the Romans.

☐ A huge storm flooded the Fens.

2f
1 mark

---

7   Draw lines to match each phrase with what it tells you about the Fens.

Phrase	The Fens are/were...
fertile soil	prone to flooding
misty vapour	not an easy place to live
complicated drainage system	damp
hostile conditions	a good place to grow crops

2a
1 mark

---

8   Which of the following descriptions best fits this passage? Tick **one**.

an historical account ☐

a traditional story partly based on real events ☐

a fairy tale ☐

a fable ☐

2f
1 mark

---

9   Mandru was brave.

Explain whether you think this is **true** or **not true**, using the story to support your answer.

_____

_____

_____

2d
2 marks

/ 10
Total for this test

Name:	Class:	Date:

Why Do You Stay Up So Late?

(1) The poet wrote this poem to explain to Russ why he stays up so late. Who do you think Russ might be? Tick the **best** answer.

the poet's dog ☐   the poet's uncle ☐

the poet's son ☐   the poet's friend ☐

☐ 2d
1 mark

---

(2) Look at these lines from the poem.

remember that day you lost two years ago
at the rockpool where you sat and played the jeweller
with all those stones you'd stolen from the shore?

What does *that day you lost* tell you here? Tick **one**.

Russ was so caught up in what he was doing that the whole day had gone before he realised it. ☐

Russ can't remember that day. ☐

Russ got lost that day. ☐

Russ wasted time that day. ☐

☐ 2a
1 mark

---

(3) Which of these words does the poet use to describe the things **he** collects? Tick **two**.

dark ☐   stony ☐   dead ☐

dull ☐   stolen ☐

☐ 2b
1 mark

---

(4) Write **one** word from the poem in each space below to complete the pairs of rhyming words. Two have been done for you.

know	ago
shore	
sleep	
surprise	eyes
	night

☐ 2g
1 mark

☐ / 4
Total for this page

5 Which of the following is the poet's **main** purpose for writing this poem?
Tick **one**.

to remember a family holiday ☐

to explain why he writes poetry ☐

to explain why he collects things ☐

to make the reader laugh ☐

2f
1 mark

---

6 The poet collects *the dull things of the day*. What do you think he means by this? Explain as fully as you can.

_____

_____

_____

2d
2 marks

---

7 Look at these lines from the poem.

one thing makes a mirror in my eyes
then I paint it with the tear to make it bright.

Why does the poet use the words *mirror* and *bright*?

_____

2g
1 mark

---

8 According to the poet, why does he stay up so late? Explain your answer as fully as you can, using **your own words**.

_____

_____

2d
2 marks

/ 10
Total for this test

This poem is by Roger McGough.

The Cats' Protection League

Midnight. A knock at the door.
Open it? Better had.
Three heavy cats, mean and bad.

They offer protection. I ask, 'What for?'
The Boss-cat snarls, 'You know the score.
Listen man and listen good

If you wanna stay in the neighbourhood,
Pay your dues or the toms will call
And wail each night on the backyard wall.

Mangle the flowers, and as for the lawn
A smelly minefield awaits you at dawn.'
These guys meant business without a doubt

Three cans of tuna, I handed them out.
They then disappeared like bats into hell
Those bad, bad cats from the CPL.

This text is from chapter four of *Tom's Midnight Garden* by Philippa Pearce.

Tom's Midnight Garden

When Tom's brother catches the measles, Tom is sent to stay with his aunt and uncle. Tom longs to play outdoors, but his aunt and uncle don't have a garden. One night, unable to sleep, Tom hears the grandfather clock in the hall strike thirteen. When Tom goes downstairs to investigate he finds a large garden at the back of the house. The next morning, angry with his aunt for lying to him about the garden, he decides to shame her into owning up.

Tom helped to clear the breakfast-table and followed his aunt to the sink. He began to dry up, darkly intent.

'Aunt Gwen.'

'Yes, Tom?'

'It was kind of you to put flowers in my bedroom when I came.'

'Tom, dear, I didn't know you'd noticed them!'

'Had you to buy them?'

'Yes, but you mustn't bother about that.'

'It would have been easier for you if you'd been able to get flowers from a garden of your own.'

'Yes, but there isn't a garden to this house, of course.'

'No?'

'What do you mean by "No", Tom?'

'I meant, What a pity! Wouldn't it be nice if there were a garden at the back of the house – with a lawn and trees and flowers and even a greenhouse?'

'It would be nice, too, if we had wings and could fly, Tom.'

'Suppose you could walk out of the door at the back this very minute, Aunt Gwen – this very minute – and walk on a lawn and cut hyacinths from the flower-beds on that lawn – from little corner-beds shaped like the quarters of an orange – what would you say, Aunt Gwen? What do you say now?'

He had as good as told her that he knew all about the garden; he had challenged her openly. Aunt Gwen did not start or show shame; she laughed.

'To begin with, Tom, I should be very surprised indeed if you picked me a hyacinth from anywhere outside, now.'

'Oh?'

'Hyacinths don't flower even out of doors at this time of year – it's too late in the summer. See what your romancing has led you into!'

'But I've *s-seen* hyacinths flowering out of doors, at just this time of year,' said Tom. He stammered because he was frightened.

'No, Tom, you can't have. They're quite over.'

Tom put down the plate he had been drying – it was still damp – and the tea cloth.

'I'm going downstairs, if you don't mind.'

Name:	Class:	Date:

The Cats' Protection League

1 In the poem the poet has some visitors. Fill in the missing information below. One has been done for you.

What time it was	
Where the poet was	At home
Who the visitors were	

2b
1 mark

- -

2 *Pay your dues or the toms will call*

Look at this line from the poem. What does *pay your dues* tell you here? Tick **one**.

The cats want the poet to respect them. ☐

The cats want the poet to give them something. ☐

The poet owes the cats money. ☐

The poet's library books are overdue. ☐

2a
1 mark

- -

3 a) The cats threaten to use the poet's lawn as a toilet.

Find and **copy one line** from the poem that tells you this.

_____

2a
1 mark

b) What **else** do the cats threaten to do?

Write **two** things in **your own words**.

1 _____

2 _____

2d
2 marks

/ 5
Total for this page

4 Why does the poet give the cats three tins of tuna? Tick **one**.

because he likes cats ☐

because he wants the cats to leave him alone ☐

because he doesn't have any cat food ☐

because cats like tuna ☐

2d
1 mark

5 The poet writes that the cats disappear *like bats into hell*. What does this suggest about the cats? Tick **two**.

They can fly. ☐   They are black. ☐

They move quickly. ☐   They hang upside down. ☐

They are evil. ☐

2g
1 mark

6 **Number** each sentence to show **the order** in which things happen in the poem.

The poet gives the cats tuna. ☐

The Boss-cat threatens the poet. ☐

The cats disappear. ☐

The poet opens the door. ☐

2f
1 mark

7 What is the **main** reason the poet wrote this poem? Tick **one**.

to entertain people ☐   to amaze people ☐

to educate people ☐   to make people think ☐

2f
1 mark

8 Cats Protection (previously called The Cats Protection League) is a charity that keeps cats safe from harm. What is a different meaning of the word *protection*, which the poet plays on in this poem? Tick **one**.

the collective noun for tomcats ☐

a promise not to harm someone if they pay you ☐

a gang of criminals ☐

a secret society of business people ☐

2g
1 mark

/ 10
Total for this test

Name:	Class:	Date:

Tom's Midnight Garden

1 Why has Tom been sent to stay with his aunt and uncle?

_____

2b
1 mark

2 *Tom's Midnight Garden* was written over fifty years ago. Find **one** clue from the passage that suggests it was not written recently.

_____

2d
1 mark

3 Read this section of the passage.

Tom helped to clear the breakfast-table and followed his aunt to the sink. He began to dry up, darkly intent.

What does the writer mean when she describes Tom as *darkly intent*? Tick **two**.

He is in a bad mood. ☐   He is quiet. ☐

He has dark circles under his eyes. ☐   He is determined. ☐

He is evil. ☐

2g
1 mark

4 Tick to show whether the following sentences about Tom are **true** or **false**. The first one has been done for you.

	True	False
Tom is angry with Aunt Gwen.	✓	
The main reason Tom mentions the flowers is because he wants to thank Aunt Gwen for putting them in his room.		
Tom thinks Aunt Gwen is lying to him about the garden.		
Tom's anger gives way to fear.		
Tom goes downstairs to wind the grandfather clock.		

2d
2 marks

/ 5
Total for this page

5 Read the following excerpt from the passage:

Aunt Gwen did not start or show shame; she laughed.
'To begin with, Tom, I should be very surprised indeed if you picked me
a hyacinth from anywhere outside, now.'
'Oh?'
'Hyacinths don't flower even out of doors at this time of year – it's
too late in the summer. See what your romancing has led you into!'
'But I've s-seen hyacinths flowering out of doors, at just this time
of year,' said Tom. He stammered because he was frightened.
'No, Tom, you can't have. They're quite over.'

What point is the writer trying to make here? Tick **one**.

Aunt Gwen is amused. ☐

It is the wrong time of year for hyacinths to flower. ☐

Tom has made a mistake. ☐

There is something strange about the garden Tom found. ☐

2d
1 mark

---

6 Which words of Aunt Gwen's suggest she is beginning to suspect Tom is not being entirely honest with her? **Find** and **copy the words** she says.

_____

2g
1 mark

---

7 Read the last part of Tom and Aunt Gwen's conversation, starting from *'Oh?'*

Find and **copy a word** that could be replaced by the phrase *vivid imagination*.

_____

2a
1 mark

---

8 Read this sentence near the end of the passage:

He stammered because he was frightened.

Why do you think Tom is frightened? Explain your answer fully, using the text to help you.

_____

_____

2d
2 marks

/ 10
Total for this test

This text is a traditional story from West Africa, adapted from *Tales of Wisdom and Wonder*, retold by Hugh Lupton.

The Blind Man and the Hunter

Once there was a blind man who lived with his sister in a hut on the edge of a forest. This blind man was very clever. 'Blind man,' people would ask, 'how is it that you are so wise?'

And the blind man would smile and say:
'Because I see with my ears.'

When the blind man's sister got married, her husband, a hunter, came to live in the hut. Every morning the hunter would go into the forest with his traps and spears. Every evening, when the hunter returned, the blind man would say: 'Please, tomorrow let me come with you, hunting in the forest.'

But the hunter would shake his head: 'What use is a man with no eyes?'

This continued for many months until one evening the hunter said: 'Very well, tomorrow you will come hunting.'

So the next morning they set off into the forest. When they came to a clearing the hunter set one of his traps, and he showed the blind man how to set another. They then made their way home.

The next morning they went back into the forest. When they came to the clearing the hunter saw there was a little grey bird in his own trap and a large, colourful bird in the blind man's trap. The hunter gave the little grey bird to the blind man and he kept the large, colourful bird for himself.

As they were walking home, the hunter asked the blind man: 'If you're so clever and you see with your ears, answer me this: why is there so much anger and hatred in this world?'

'Because the world is full of people like you - who take what is not theirs.'

The hunter took the little grey bird out of the blind man's hand and gave him the large, colourful one. 'I'm sorry,' he said.

They walked on. A little later the hunter asked: 'If you're so clever and you see with your ears, answer me this: why is there so much love and kindness in this world?'

'Because the world is full of people like you - who learn from their mistakes.'

And from that day onwards, if the hunter heard anyone ask: 'Blind man, how is it that you are so wise?' He would put his arm around the blind man's shoulders and say:

'Because he sees with his ears…and hears with his heart.'

This text is adapted from *Ten Freaky Forces of Nature* by Douglas E. Richards from www.ngkids.co.uk

Five Freaky Forces of Nature

5

Nature can be unbelievably powerful. Everyone knows about earthquakes, hurricanes, blizzards, avalanches, forest fires, floods, tidal waves, and even thunderstorms. But if you thought Mother Nature didn't have many surprises up her sleeve, think again. Nature has a load of other powers that, while less well known, can only be described as, well, freaky.

- **Dodge balls**   About 1,000 years ago hundreds of people were mysteriously killed in the Himalayan Mountains. A recent investigation concluded that they were caught in a hailstorm that dropped chunks of ice the size of cricket balls on their heads at more than 160 km per hour. Hail is formed when raindrops are carried into extremely cold areas of the atmosphere by powerful vertical winds. The longer the tiny specks of ice bounce around, the bigger they become. When the clumps of ice grow too big for the wind to hold up, they fall to the ground as hail.

- **It's raining frogs!**   Small frogs rained on a town in Serbia, sending residents running for cover. 'I thought maybe a plane carrying frogs had exploded in mid-air,' one resident told a local newspaper. Had the town gone crazy? Probably not. Scientists believe that tornadoes can suck up the surfaces of lakes and other bodies of water. When they do, they can take frogs and fish along for the ride. The tornadoes can then drop them miles away.

- **Gas attack**   When a volcano erupts, a glowing sea of molten lava often flows down its sides, destroying everything in its path. A lava flow is unbelievably dangerous. But a volcano can produce something even deadlier: a pyroclastic flow, which is a cloud of gas and rock that can reach temperatures above 500°C. The flow crashes down the side of a volcano like an avalanche, typically reaching speeds of more than 80 km per hour.

- **Great balls of fire**   During a thunderstorm, a glowing ball the size of your head suddenly appears. It hovers a few feet above the ground, drops down, dances across the garden, and then darts up into the air before it fades away. This freaky phenomenon is ball lightning. Some scientists think that when normal lightning strikes the ground, it vaporises a mineral called silicon found in soil. They think this silicon forms a kind of bubble that burns in the oxygen around it.

- **Snowball factory**   You head outside after a snowstorm and see dozens of log- or drum-shaped snowballs. These rare creations are called snow rollers, and Mother Nature makes them all by herself. Snow rollers form when wet snow falls on ground that is icy, so snow won't stick to it. Pushed by strong winds, the snow rolls into logs. Maybe this is nature's way of saying it's time for a snowball fight!

Name:	Class:	Date:

The Blind Man and the Hunter

(1) Fill in the missing information about the story. One has been done for you.

Where the hut was	
Who the blind man lived with	his sister
Who the hunter was	

<table><tr><td>1 mark</td><td>2b</td></tr></table>

---

(2) Which of the following **best** describes the blind man? Tick **one**.

happy ☐   patient ☐   honest ☐   wise ☐

<table><tr><td>1 mark</td><td>2c</td></tr></table>

---

(3) a) Why did the hunter refuse to take the blind man hunting with him at first?

_____

<table><tr><td>1 mark</td><td>2b</td></tr></table>

b) Why do you think the hunter eventually agreed to take the blind man hunting with him?

_____

<table><tr><td>1 mark</td><td>2d</td></tr></table>

---

(4) The blind man says that he *sees with his ears*.

What does he mean by this? Tick the **best** answer.

He cannot see with his eyes. ☐

He can see things with his ears. ☐

He uses his sense of hearing to work out what's happening. ☐

He cannot hear very well. ☐

<table><tr><td>1 mark</td><td>2a</td></tr></table>

<table><tr><td>/ 5</td></tr><tr><td>Total for this page</td></tr></table>

5 **Number** these events to show **the order** in which they happen in the story. The first one has been done for you.

[ ] The hunter finds a bird caught in each trap.

[ ] The hunter apologises to the blind man.

[1] The hunter comes to live with the blind man and his sister.

[ ] The blind man and the hunter set traps.

[ ] The blind man asks the hunter if he can go hunting with him.

2f
1 mark

---

6 *he kept the large, colourful bird for himself*

What does this phrase tell you about the hunter? Tick **two**.

He is dishonest. [ ]   He is selfish. [ ]

He is cruel. [ ]   He is clever. [ ]

2g
1 mark

---

7 This story is a fable with a lesson to be learned. Which of the following 'lessons' would **best** fit the story? Tick **one**.

It is important to learn from your mistakes. [ ]

It is important to apologise if you have done something wrong. [ ]

It is important to listen carefully. [ ]

It is important to respect people who are blind. [ ]

2c
1 mark

---

8 a) What is the hunter's attitude towards the blind man at the **beginning** of the story? Explain your answer, using the text to help you.

_____

_____

2d
1 mark

b) What is the hunter's attitude towards the blind man at the **end** of the story? Explain your answer, using the text to help you.

_____

_____

2d
1 mark

/ 10
Total for this test

Name:	Class:	Date:

Five Freaky Forces of Nature

1 a) When and where were hundreds of people killed by hailstones?

• When? _____

• Where? _____

2b
1 mark

b) The writer describes the people who died as being *mysteriously killed*.
Why do you think their deaths were a mystery to start with?

_____

2d
1 mark

2 Draw lines to match each word or phrase with its meaning in the text.
One has been done for you.

a fast-moving cloud of rock and gas emitted by an erupting volcano

tornado —— a funnel-shaped spinning windstorm

snow roller

pyroclastic flow — a mineral found in the soil

hail — frozen rain

silicon — a log- or drum-shaped snowball created by the wind

2a
1 mark

3 Read the introductory paragraph, starting *Nature can be…*

What does this paragraph tell you about nature?
Write **two** things in **your own words**.

1 _____

2 _____

2d
2 marks

/ 5
Total for this page

4 *'I thought maybe a plane carrying frogs had exploded in mid-air,' one resident told a local newspaper.*

What impression does this give of the day when frogs rained on a town in Serbia? Tick **two**.

The town was near an airport. ☐

The resident was mad. ☐

The resident heard an explosion. ☐

The 'frog rain' started suddenly. ☐

A lot of Serbian planes carry frogs. ☐

There were a lot of frogs. ☐

2d
1 mark

5 Read the paragraph headed *Gas attack*.

Look at these words that the writer uses in the paragraph.

destroying   dangerous   deadlier   crashes

Why has the writer used these words?

_____

2g
1 mark

6 Where would you expect to find this text? Tick the **best** answer.

in a newspaper ☐   in an encyclopaedia ☐

in a magazine ☐   in an advertising brochure ☐

2f
1 mark

7 *Nature can be unbelievably powerful.*

From what you learn in the passage, do you think this is **true**?
Explain as fully as you can, using the text to help you answer.

_____

_____

_____

2d
2 marks

/ 10
Total for this test

Answers and mark schemes

Autumn test 1: Part A – Growing Up in Ancient Greece

	Part A: *Growing Up in Ancient Greece*	Content domain	Mark	Extra information
1	Award 1 mark for mentioning one of the following points: • A son would look after his parents in old age. • A daughter had to take a wedding gift or dowry.	2b	1	
2	A/the father	2b	1	
3	boys whose parents were not poor ✓	2d	1	
4	Because the weather was warm and dry. ✓	2d	1	
5	Award 1 mark for mentioning **both** of the following: • from pictures (on pottery vases) • from objects (found by archaeologists)	2b	1	
6	Award 1 mark for one or more of the following points: • to break the text up • to make the text easier to read • to tell readers what each section or paragraph is going to be about • to make it easier for readers to find the information they want	2f	1	
7	Award 1 mark for **all three** of the following answers **and** no others ticked: Many school subjects from Ancient Greece are still studied in schools today. ✓ Girls learned different things to boys. ✓ Some of the equipment used in Ancient Greek schools is no longer used in schools today. ✓	2b	1	
8	in a history book ✓	2f	1	
9	If the pupil argues that the statement is **true** (i.e. that girls in Ancient Greece **did** have a better life than boys): Award 1 mark for mentioning one or more of the following points: • Girls' work was easier than boys' work. • Girls could stay at home but boys had to go to school. • Boys had to prepare for war as soldiers. Award 1 mark for including an appropriate reference to the text to support the point(s). If the pupil argues that the statement is **not true** (i.e. that girls in Ancient Greece **did not** have a better life than boys): Award 1 mark for mentioning one or more of the following points: • Girl babies were more likely to be unwanted and abandoned. • Girls did not get the chance to go to school. • Most girls did not learn to read and write. Award 1 mark for including an appropriate reference to the text to support the point(s).	2d	2	

Autumn test 1: Part B – Oliver Twist

	Part B: *Oliver Twist*	Content domain	Mark	Extra information
1a	Award 1 mark for one of the following points: • He collapses on a (cold) doorstep. • He is *too exhausted to beg*. • He staggers (up to the window).	2a	1	
1b	Award 1 mark for one of the following points: • He stares longingly at the bread, cakes, buns and pies/through the bakery window. • When Dodger asks him if he's hungry he says '*Very*'. • He gobbles the food Dodger brings him.	2a	1	
2	Award 1 mark for each of the following points: • They walk differently (Oliver staggers and Dodger swaggers). • Dodger is confident and Oliver isn't. • Oliver is hungry and Dodger isn't. • Dodger has somewhere to live and Oliver doesn't. • Dodger knows his way around the city and Oliver doesn't. • Dodger has money and Oliver doesn't.	2d	1	
3	*ragged urchins*	2a	1	
4	He is sly. ✓	2g	1	
5	Award 1 mark for any **two** of the following points: • He is polite. • He is patient. • He can creep/move quietly. • He can handle objects delicately/carefully. • He is a natural thief/pickpocket.	2b	1	
6	Award 1 mark for one of the following points, providing it is backed up by an appropriate explanation: • proud because he has done well in Fagin's game • full/refreshed/less exhausted because he has eaten • grateful/relieved because he has found a new 'family' • wary because of Fagin's leering grin	2d	1	
7	Award 1 mark for one of the following: • historical fiction • realistic fiction • narrative • fiction Award 1 mark for making appropriate reference to the text that supports one of the four answers given above.	2f	2	
8	Award 1 mark for reference to one or more of the following points: • It is dirty. • The people are poor. • The buildings are crumbling. • It is an unpleasant place.	2c	1	

Autumn test 2: Part A – Colly's Barn

Part A: *Colly's Barn*	Content domain	Mark	Extra information
1	lightning ☑	2b	1	
2	Award 2 marks for answers that reference the text, e.g.: • *They're two of the birds the writer mentions at the beginning of the paragraph: '…the birds in the barn huddled together in their nests…'* • *They're animals of some sort, because they sleep in a barn.* Award 1 mark for answers that correctly identify Colly is a swallow and Screecher is an owl/they are birds but without further reference to the text, e.g.: *I know Colly is a swallow and Screecher is an owl, because I've read the story.*	2d	2	Do not accept answers that use wider knowledge rather than answers based on the text, e.g.: *Colly might be a dog because a collie is a type of dog and Screecher might be an owl because owls make a screeching noise.*
3	Award 1 mark for any **two** of the following: *alliteration, personification, onomatopoeia.*	2g	1	
4	Award 1 mark for one of the following points supported by an appropriate explanation (examples of explanations given here in brackets): • The writer starts the paragraph by describing a peaceful scene. (This makes the sudden lightning strike more exciting in comparison.) • The writer uses exaggeration, describing the thunder as *deafening* and the lightning as *blinding*. (This adds to the excitement by creating drama.) • The writer describes something unusual and dangerous – the *fireball* of ball lightning. (The unfamiliarity and danger both add to the excitement.)	2g	1	
5	She loves Grandad. ☑	2d	1	
6	pristine ☑	2a	1	
7	They are very close. ☑	2a	1	
8	[1] The birds huddle together in their nests. [5] Annie's father decides to pull down the barn. [2] Screecher peers through a crack in the wall. [4] Annie's father and mother discover the hole in the barn wall. [3] The barn gets damaged.	2f	1	Award 1 mark for all events correctly numbered.
9	an animal story ☑	2f	1	

Autumn test 2: Part B – Mercury

	Part B: *Mercury*	Content domain	Mark	Extra information
1	Award 1 mark for: It was named after the messenger of the Roman gods **because it moves so fast.**	2b	1	
2	(see table below)	2b	2	Award 2 marks for all five statements correctly marked. Award 1 mark for three or four statements correctly marked.
3	(see matching below)	2b	1	Award 1 mark for all four correctly matched.
4	Award 1 mark for one of the following points: • Because Mercury is (three times/so much/a lot) closer to the Sun than the Earth is. • Because the Sun is (three times/so much/a lot) closer.	2d	1	
5	Award 1 mark for one or more of the following points: • to break the text up • to make the text easier to read • to tell readers what each section or paragraph is going to be about • to make it easier for readers to find the information they want	2f	1	
6	a report ☑	2f	1	
7	You can't see Mercury from Earth very often. ☑	2b	1	
8	Award 1 mark for one or more of the following points: • no atmosphere/vacuum of space • extreme temperatures • dangerous radiation Award 1 mark for one or more of these points being supported by a quote from the text.	2d	2	

Question 2:

Statement	✓ or ✗
Mercury is the largest planet.	✗
Mercury is the fastest moving planet.	✓
Mercury is the planet closest to the Sun.	✓
Mercury is the hottest planet.	✗
Mercury is the planet with the widest range of temperatures.	✓

Question 3:

Measurement	Fact
427°C	the night-time temperature on Mercury
1,500 km	the daytime temperature on Mercury
4,879.4 km	the average speed at which Mercury orbits the Sun
172,332 km per hour	the diameter of Mercury
–173°C	the width of the Caloris Basin

Spring test 1: Part A – The Missing Boy

	Part A: *The Missing Boy*			Content domain	Mark	Extra information
1	Award 1 mark for: *a bus/(on a poster) on the bus.*			2b	1	Do not accept: *a poster/on a poster.*
2	The boy in the poster looks like her son. ☑			2g	1	
3	Award 1 mark for mentioning **two** of the following features being similar or the same: • hair • skin • eyes • sneakers			2b	1	
4a	Award 1 mark for: *No* or any answer implying it.			2d	1	
4b	Award 1 mark for answers that refer to the following concept: • *This is how the poet's son describes himself./The poet is writing from her son's point of view.*			2g	1	
5		True	False	2d	2	Award 2 marks for all three ticks correctly placed. Award 1 mark for two ticks correctly placed. Award no marks for one tick correctly placed.
	The poet's son is a lot older than the missing boy.		✓ (given)			
	The poet's son finds the poster upsetting.	✓				
	The poster has been on the bus for a long time.	✓				
	The poet's son knows the missing boy.		✓			
6	Award 1 mark for the following words underlined: *my son holds my hand tight* or *holds my hand tight*			2g	1	
7	the poet's son ☑			2c	1	
8	realistic ☑			2f	1	

Spring test 1: Part B – Room 13

	Part B: *Room 13*	Content domain	Mark	Extra information
1	alone ☑ afraid ☑	2b	1	Award 1 mark for **both** and **only** these words ticked.
2	to set the mood of the story ☑	2f	1	
3	Award 1 mark for **one** of the following points from the text. Award 1 mark for an appropriate explanation of how this aspect of the text adds to the scariness of the paragraph. (Examples given in brackets.) • As Fliss climbed the stairs it grew colder. (This doesn't happen in real life.) • Door 13 swung inward with a squeal. (Doors don't swing open by themselves in real life, and a squealing noise can be scary.) • The door that swings open is number 13. (Some people think 13 is an unlucky number.) • Fliss's feet carried her over the threshold. (Fliss isn't in control of where she goes.) • The voice hissed, 'The Room of Doom.' (The word 'doom' suggests something bad is going to happen. The voice is hissing, which is scary.)	2g	2	Both a point from the text **and** an explanation of how this adds to the scariness of the paragraph are needed for answers to be awarded 2 marks.
4	<table><tr><td></td><td>True</td><td>False</td></tr><tr><td>The house is near the sea.</td><td>✓ (given)</td><td></td></tr><tr><td>The animal depicted on the gate is a bat.</td><td></td><td>✓</td></tr><tr><td>Fliss pushes open the door to Room 13.</td><td></td><td>✓</td></tr><tr><td>Fliss is afraid of Room 13 even before she sees what is inside.</td><td>✓</td><td></td></tr></table>	2b	1	Award 1 mark for three ticks correctly placed.
5	*Her feet carried her over the threshold*	2a	1	
6	*damp and trembling*	2a	1	
7	Award 1 mark for any of the following points: • to heighten tension • to make the passage more frightening • to introduce a sense of dread • to add a supernatural element	2g	1	
8	Award 1 mark for: a coffin. Award 1 mark for one or more of the following explanations referencing the text: • because the box fills Fliss with horror • because the box smells of damp earth • because the box is called 'The Bed of Dread' • because there is a shape like a body in the box/the shape is a body because it sits up	2d	2	

Spring test 2: Part A – The Legend of the Fens

	Part A: *The Legend of the Fens*	Content domain	Mark	Extra information
1	Award 1 mark for: a large area of flat, low-lying land (in eastern England).	2b	1	
2	*or so the Romans thought*	2g	1	
3	Award 1 mark for **two** of the following points: • He escaped from the Romans. • He went into hiding. • He made plans. • He was clever. • He was sly. • He was careful. • He knew how to engage with the local gods of water and the sky.	2b	1	
4	Award 1 mark for any of the following points: • He did not want the Romans to capture him again. • He knew the Romans would be looking for him. • He knew the Romans would kill him if they found him. • He wanted to be able to carry out his plans without the Romans stopping him.	2d	1	
5	The writer admires the Celts. ✓	2g	1	
6	4 A stranger came to town with a warning. 1 The Romans captured Mandru's daughter, Rowena. 3 The Romans captured Mandru and his warriors. 2 Mandru made plans to overthrow the Romans. 5 A huge storm flooded the Fens.	2f	1	Award 1 mark for **all** events numbered correctly.
7	**Phrase** **The Fens are/were...** fertile soil — a good place to grow crops misty vapour — damp complicated drainage system — not an easy place to live hostile conditions — prone to flooding	2a	1	Award 1 mark for all lines drawn correctly.
8	a traditional story partly based on real events ✓	2f	1	
9	If the pupil agrees that the statement is **true** (i.e. that Mandru **was** brave): Award 1 mark for mentioning one or more of the following justifications for this opinion: • When he heard his daughter had been captured he made plans to overthrow (i.e. fight) the Romans. • Even though he was in hiding he showed his face in public, risking capture, in order to warn the Celts about the storm. Award 1 mark for including an appropriate reference to the text to support this. If the pupil argues that the statement is **not true** (i.e. that Mandru was **not** brave): Award 1 mark for mentioning one or more of the following justifications for this opinion: • When the Romans captured him he ran away. • He went into hiding. • He got the gods to defeat the Romans for him, instead of fighting them himself. Award 1 mark for including an appropriate reference to the text to support this.	2d	2	

Spring test 2: Part B – Why Do You Stay Up So Late?

	Part B: *Why Do You Stay Up So Late?*	Content domain	Mark	Extra information
1	the poet's son ✓	2d	1	
2	Russ was so caught up in what he was doing that the whole day had gone before he realised it. ✓	2a	1	
3	dull ✓ dead ✓	2b	1	Award 1 mark for **both** and **only** these answers ticked.
4	<table><tr><td>know</td><td>ago</td></tr><tr><td>shore</td><td>*more*</td></tr><tr><td>sleep</td><td>*keep*</td></tr><tr><td>surprise</td><td>eyes</td></tr><tr><td>*bright*</td><td>night</td></tr></table>	2g	1	Award 1 mark for all three missing words correct.
5	to explain why he writes poetry ✓	2f	1	
6	Award 1 mark for each of the following points, up to a maximum of 2 marks: • **Things** may refer to: events (things that have happened)/thoughts/impressions (things the poet has seen). • The poet describes these things as *dull* because they are ordinary.	2d	2	
7	Award 1 mark for answers that refer to showing that the *one thing* is special/different/attracts attention/not dull.	2g	1	
8	Award 1 mark for each of the following points, up to a maximum of 2 marks: • to go through the day's events/impressions/thoughts and find the most interesting/special ones • to make the special ones even more special (by writing about them) • to write poetry (about them)	2d	2	

Summer test 1: Part A – The Cats' Protection League

	Part A: *The Cats' Protection League*		Content domain	Mark	Extra information
1	What time it was / *Midnight* Where the poet was / *At home* Who the visitors were / *Three cats/three heavy cats/three heavy cats, mean and bad*		2b	1	Award 1 mark for both answers correct.
2	The cats want the poet to give them something. ✓		2a	1	
3a	*a smelly minefield (awaits you at dawn)*		2a	1	
3b	Award 1 mark **each** for the following points (here quoted directly from the poem) that is expressed in the **pupil's own words**. • *wail each night on the backyard wall* • *mangle the flowers*		2d	2	
4	because he wants the cats to leave him alone ✓		2d	1	
5	They move They are evil		2g	1	Award 1 mark for **both** and **only** these answers ticked.
6	The poet gives the cats tuna. ☐ 3 The Boss-cat threatens the poet. ☐ 2 The cats disappear. ☐ 4 The poet opens the door. ☐ 1		2f	1	Award 1 mark for all four sentences numbered correctly.
7	to entertain people ✓		2f	1	
8	a promise not to harm someone if they pay you ✓		2g	1	

Summer test 1: Part B – Tom's Midnight Garden

	Part B: *Tom's Midnight Garden*			Content domain	Mark	Extra information
1	Award 1 mark for either of the following points: • Because his brother has got the measles • So that he doesn't catch the measles			2b	1	
2	Award 1 mark for any of the following points: • Tom's brother catches the measles. • There's a grandfather clock in the hall. • The characters' speech is old-fashioned in places (e.g. Tom says *'Had you to buy them?'* instead of *'Did you have to buy them?'*). • The writer uses the word *tea cloth* instead of *tea towel*. • Tom is drying up so Aunt Gwen doesn't have a dishwasher.			2d	1	
3	He is in a bad mood. ☑ He is determined. ☑			2g	1	Award 1 mark for **both** and **only** these answers ticked.
4		True	False	2d	2	Award 2 marks for all four answers correct. Award 1 mark for three correct answers.
	Tom is angry with Aunt Gwen.	✓ (given)				
	The main reason Tom mentions the flowers is because he wants to thank Aunt Gwen for putting them in his room.		✓			
	Tom thinks Aunt Gwen is lying to him about the garden.	✓				
	Tom's anger gives way to fear.	✓				
	Tom goes downstairs to wind the grandfather clock.		✓			
5	There is something strange about the garden Tom found. ☑			2d	1	
6	*'What do you mean by "No", Tom?'*			2g	1	
7	*romancing*			2a	1	

8	Award 1 mark for making a sensible suggestion of why Tom might be frightened, e.g.:
	 • *the garden won't be there:*
	    (because/and/or)...
	    ○ *he imagined/dreamed the garden*
	    ○ *there's something strange about the garden*
	    ○ *the garden is from another time*
	    ○ *he's going mad*
	
	 Award 1 mark for supporting the suggestion using appropriate reference to the text.
				2d	2	

Summer test 2: Part A – The Blind Man and the Hunter

	Part A: *The Blind Man and the Hunter*		Content domain	Mark	Extra information
1	**Where the hut was** · *on the edge of a forest* **Who the blind man lived with** · his sister **Who the hunter was** · *the husband of the blind man's sister*		2b	1	Award 1 mark for **both** pieces of missing information filled in correctly.
2	wise ☑		2c	1	
3a	Award 1 mark for answers that refer to the fact that he thought the blind man would be of no use.		2b	1	
3b	Award 1 mark for any plausible explanation of why the hunter eventually agreed to take the blind man hunting with him, e.g.: • *because he got tired of the blind man asking* • *because he was in a good mood that day* • *because he had had time to get to know the blind man better*		2d	1	
4	He uses his sense of hearing to work out what's happening. ☑		2a	1	
5	[4] The hunter finds a bird caught in each trap. [5] The hunter apologises to the blind man. [1] The hunter comes to live with the blind man and his sister. [3] The blind man and the hunter set traps. [2] The blind man asks the hunter if he can go hunting with him.		2f	1	Award 1 mark for **all** the events numbered correctly.
6	He is dishonest. ☑ He is selfish. ☑		2g	1	Award 1 mark for **both** and **only** these answers ticked.
7	It is important to learn from your mistakes.		2c	1	
8a	Award 1 mark for one of the following points provided it is supported by an appropriate reference to the text: • He thinks the blind man is useless. • He does not respect the blind man. • He is not friendly towards the blind man.		2d	1	
8b	Award 1 mark for one or more of the following points that make appropriate reference to the text (examples of appropriate references given in brackets): • He is friendly towards him. (*He puts his arm around the blind man's shoulders.*) • He respects him. (*He pays the blind man a compliment (by saying that he hears with his heart).*)		2d	1	

Summer test 2: Part B – Five Freaky Forces of Nature

	Part B: *Five Freaky Forces of Nature*	Content domain	Mark	Extra information
1a	Award 1 mark for both correct facts: • **When?** About 1,000 years ago • **Where?** In the Himalayan Mountains	2b	1	
1b	Award 1 mark for any answer mentioning that the hail would have melted.	2d	1	
2		2a	1	Award 1 mark for all lines drawn correctly.
3	Award 1 mark for each of the following points, up to a maximum of 2 marks: • Nature is very powerful. • Nature demonstrates its power in many different ways. • Some of nature's powers are surprising/unusual/strange.	2d	2	
4	The 'frog rain' started suddenly. ☑ There were a lot of frogs. ☑	2d	1	Award 1 mark for **both** and **only** these answers ticked.
5	Award 1 mark for either of the following points: • to make it exciting to read • to emphasise how dangerous/violent a volcanic eruption is	2g	1	
6	in a magazine ☑	2f	1	
7	Award 1 mark for agreeing that the statement is **true and** backing it up with **one** example below. Award 2 marks for agreeing that the statement is **true and** backing it up with **two or more** examples below. Examples: • *Hailstones can kill people/can reach the size of cricket balls/can travel at over 160 km per hour.* • *Tornadoes can suck up frogs (and fish) and drop them miles away.* • *Molten lava destroys everything in its path.* • *Pyroclastic flows reach temperatures above 500°C and speeds of more than 80 km per hour.* • *Lightning can vaporise silicon in the soil.* • *Strong winds can roll snow into logs.*	2d	2	

Coverage grid

Test	Question	Content domain	Strand	Marks
Autumn test 1				
Part A (non-fiction)	1	2b	Comprehension	1
	2	2b	Comprehension	1
	3	2d	Making inferences	1
	4	2b	Making inferences	1
	5	2b	Comprehension	1
	6	2f	Themes and conventions	1
	7	2b	Comprehension	1
	8	2f	Themes and conventions	1
	9	2d	Making inferences	2
Part B (fiction)	1a	2a	Comprehension	1
	1b	2a	Comprehension	1
	2	2d	Making inferences	1
	3	2a	Comprehension	1
	4	2g	Language for effect	1
	5	2b	Comprehension	1
	6	2d	Making inferences	1
	7	2f	Themes and conventions	2
	8	2c	Comprehension	1
Autumn test 2				
Part A (fiction)	1	2b	Comprehension	1
	2	2d	Making inferences	2
	3	2g	Language for effect	1
	4	2g	Language for effect	1
	5	2d	Making inferences	1
	6	2a	Comprehension	1
	7	2a	Comprehension	1
	8	2f	Themes and conventions	1
	9	2f	Themes and conventions	1
Part B (non-fiction)	1	2b	Comprehension	1
	2	2b	Comprehension	2
	3	2b	Comprehension	1
	4	2d	Making inferences	1
	5	2f	Themes and conventions	1
	6	2f	Themes and conventions	1
	7	2b	Comprehension	1
	8	2d	Making inferences	2

Test	Question	Content domain	Strand	Marks
Spring test 1				
Part A (poetry)	1	2b	Comprehension	1
	2	2g	Language for effect	1
	3	2b	Comprehension	1
	4a	2d	Making inferences	1
	4b	2g	Making inferences	1
	5	2d	Making inferences	2
	6	2g	Language for effect	1
	7	2c	Comprehension	1
	8	2f	Themes and conventions	1
Part B (fiction)	1	2b	Comprehension	1
	2	2f	Comprehension	1
	3	2g	Language for effect	2
	4	2b	Making inferences	1
	5	2a	Comprehension	1
	6	2a	Comprehension	1
	7	2g	Language for effect	1
	8	2d	Making inferences	2
Spring test 2				
Part A (non-fiction)	1	2b	Comprehension	1
	2	2g	Comprehension	1
	3	2b	Comprehension	1
	4	2d	Making inferences	1
	5	2g	Comprehension	1
	6	2f	Themes and conventions	1
	7	2a	Language for effect	1
	8	2f	Themes and conventions	1
	9	2d	Making inferences	2
Part B (poetry)	1	2d	Making inferences	1
	2	2a	Comprehension	1
	3	2b	Comprehension	1
	4	2g	Language for effect	1
	5	2f	Comprehension	1
	6	2d	Making inferences	2
	7	2g	Language for effect	1
	8	2d	Making inferences	2

Test	Question	Content domain	Strand	Marks
Summer test 1				
Part A (poetry)	1	2b	Comprehension	1
	2	2a	Comprehension	1
	3a	2a	Comprehension	1
	3b	2d	Making inferences	2
	4	2d	Making inferences	1
	5	2g	Language for effect	1
	6	2f	Themes and conventions	1
	7	2f	Comprehension	1
	8	2g	Language for effect	1
Part B (fiction)	1	2b	Comprehension	1
	2	2d	Themes and conventions	1
	3	2g	Language for effect	1
	4	2d	Making inferences	2
	5	2d	Comprehension	1
	6	2g	Making inferences	1
	7	2a	Comprehension	1
	8	2d	Making inferences	2
Summer test 2				
Part A (fiction)	1	2b	Comprehension	1
	2	2c	Comprehension	1
	3a	2b	Comprehension	1
	3b	2d	Making inferences	1
	4	2a	Making inferences	1
	5	2f	Themes and conventions	1
	6	2g	Language for effect	1
	7	2c	Comprehension	1
	8a	2d	Making inferences	1
	8b	2d	Making inferences	1
Part B (non-fiction)	1a	2b	Comprehension	1
	1b	2d	Making inferences	1
	2	2a	Comprehension	1
	3	2d	Making inferences	2
	4	2d	Language for effect	1
	5	2g	Language for effect	1
	6	2f	Themes and conventions	1
	7	2d	Comprehension	2